Violin
93VN

# Doris Gazda & Albert S

## Level 2
### TECHNIQUE AND PROGRAM MUSIC FOR STRING ORCHESTRA AND INDIVIDUAL INSTRUCTION

## CONTENTS

**Spotlight on Strings, Level 2** is available for Violin, Viola, Cello, String Bass, Teacher Score/Keyboard.

ISBN 0-8497-3346-4

© **1997 Neil A. Kjos Music Company**, 4380 Jutland Drive, San Diego, California, 92117.
International copyright secured. All rights reserved. Printed in U.S.A.

# INTRODUCTION

By now you have discovered the joy of playing your instrument. Now it's time to continue with more opportunities to become an accomplished string player.

As you learned in Level 1, for you to be successful you must:

1. Try as hard as you can to do everything correctly.
2. Find a time and place to practice regularly at home.
3. Ask your family to listen to you play your pieces.
4. Remember to bring your instrument and music to school on your lesson day. Have a pencil with you, too.

Here are some reminders for caring for your violin:

1. Keep it in the case when you are not playing it. Make sure your case is completely closed and latched before picking it up.
2. Clean it with a soft cloth before you put it away.
3. Store it where it will not get too hot or cold.
4. Until you have learned to tune your instrument, ask your teacher to tune the strings. Also have your teacher check the bridge and other parts of the instrument for general maintenance.

Here are some reminders to help you care for your bow:

1. Each time you play your violin, tighten your bow so that a pencil will just barely slide between the hair and the stick.
2. Rosin the bow about 10 times back and forth before you play.
3. Wipe off the stick and loosen the hair before you put the bow back into the case.
4. Do not touch the hair at any time.

## Special Features in Spotlight on Strings, Level 2

### IMPROVISING MUSIC

When you make up music and play it without writing it down, you are improvising. Sometimes you can improvise a few notes in the middle of a piece that is already composed. Other times, you may wish to make up melodies of your own. You will be given suggestions for improvising as you progress through **Spotlight on Strings, Level 2**. Use those suggestions as a starting place for your own ideas about where and when to improvise.

All of the great composers improvised music. Sometimes they wrote down their improvisations which then became compositions that you play today. One of the best ways to listen to improvisation today is in the field of jazz. Many great jazz string players play concerts and have made excellent recordings. Try improvising in many different ways and have a good time with it!

### WRITING MUSIC

Writing music is a wonderful adventure. In **Spotlight on Strings, Level 2**, you will learn how to write music on the staff and will also have the opportunity to write your own compositions. You may wish to try writing more music than there is room for in this book. For that, you will need a manuscript book. Once you learn how to write music by hand, then you may wish to investigate the possibilities for writing music at the computer. There are many computer programs for writing music and you should seek advice and recommendations from your teacher before acquiring software for your computer. No matter if you compose with manuscript paper or computer, always play the music that you write so that you are sure it is written the way you want it to sound.

# I RHYTHM REVIEW

| Names | Notes | Rests | Duration in $\frac{4}{4}$ , $\frac{3}{4}$ , & $\frac{2}{4}$ Time Signatures |
|---|---|---|---|
| Whole | o | ▬ | four beats of sound or silence |
| Half | 𝅗𝅥 or | ▬ | two beats of sound or silence |
| Quarter | ♩ or | 𝄽 | one beat of sound or silence |
| Eighth | ♪ or | 𝄾 | 1/2 beat of sound or silence |
| Two Eighths | ♫ | 𝄽 | one beat of sound or silence |

**Beats** - Steady pulses felt or heard in music like ticks of a clock.

## TIME SIGNATURES

$\frac{4}{4}$ $\left(\frac{4}{𝅗𝅥}\right)$ $\left(\frac{4}{𝄽}\right)$ four beats in a measure / a quarter note or quarter rest receives one beat

$\frac{2}{4}$ $\left(\frac{2}{𝅗𝅥}\right)$ $\left(\frac{2}{𝄽}\right)$ two beats in a measure / a quarter note or quarter rest receives one beat

$\frac{3}{4}$ $\left(\frac{3}{𝅗𝅥}\right)$ $\left(\frac{3}{𝄽}\right)$ three beats in a measure / a quarter note or quarter rest receives one beat.

## Rhythm Studies

*Play on each open string.*
1. Arco on any pitch.
2. Left or right hand pizzicato.

### 1. Rhythm Study in $\frac{4}{4}$ Time

### 2. Rhythm Study in $\frac{2}{4}$ Time

In $\frac{2}{4}$ time, a whole rest receives two beats of silence.

### 3. Rhythm Study in $\frac{3}{4}$ Time with a Pick-Up Note

*Improvising Music*

Select $\frac{4}{4}$ , $\frac{2}{4}$ or $\frac{3}{4}$ time signature and improvise a short rhythm on one open string.
Play your rhythm arco or pizzicato with any one note or combination of notes.
Teach it to your class.

# II MAJOR & MINOR FINGERING PATTERNS

## MAJOR FINGERING PATTERN

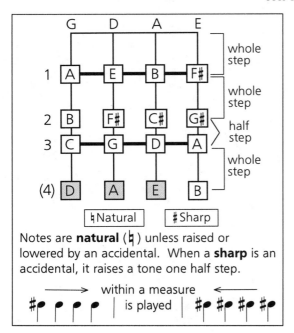

Notes are **natural** (♮) unless raised or lowered by an accidental. When a **sharp** is an accidental, it raises a tone one half step.

within a measure ← ——— is played ———

In the major fingering pattern, the distance between the 1st finger down and the 2nd finger down is a **whole step**.

The distance between the 2nd finger down and the 3rd finger down is a **half step**.

(4) means optional 4th finger

## MINOR FINGERING PATTERN

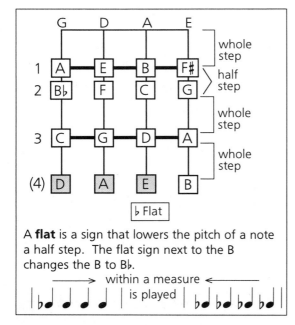

A **flat** is a sign that lowers the pitch of a note a half step. The flat sign next to the B changes the B to B♭.

within a measure ← ——— is played ———

In the minor fingering pattern, the distance between the 1st finger down and the 2nd finger down is a **half step.**

The distance between the 2nd finger down and the 3rd finger down is a **whole step**.

(4) means optional 4th finger

# MAJOR AND MINOR FINGERING PATTERN STUDIES IN $\frac{4}{4}$ TIME

### 1. G String - MAJOR Fingering Pattern

### 2. G String - MINOR Fingering Pattern

### 3. D String - MAJOR Fingering Pattern

### 4. D String - MINOR Fingering Pattern

A natural ( ♮ ) before a note means that the note is neither flat nor sharp.

### 5. A String - MAJOR Fingering Pattern

### 6. A String - MINOR Fingering Pattern

### 7. E String - MAJOR Fingering Pattern    *Violin and Bass only.*

### 8. E String - MINOR Fingering Pattern    *Violin and Bass only.*

*Improvising Music*

Make up your own melody using either the major or minor fingering pattern on any one string. It may be different each time you play it.

# MELODIES AND CHROMATIC STUDIES IN $\frac{2}{4}$ TIME

| Chromatic | Fermata |
|---|---|
|  | |
| A passage of music is chromatic when it is written or played in half steps. | Hold a note or rest somewhat longer than its written value. |

### 1. Are You Sleeping?

Traditional Round

Play *Are You Sleeping?* as written. Then change some of the quarter notes to sets of two eighth notes. Change the half notes any way you wish.

*Improvising Music*

FINGERING: 1_____ A line following a fingering means to keep that finger down.
③ A fingering in a circle means place only that finger on the string.

### 2. Bingo

American Camp Song

### 3. Major and Minor Fingering Patterns Combined

a. *Chromatic Pattern*   FINGERING: Slide the 2nd finger on the string.

b.   c.

### 4. Locomotive

# MELODIES IN ¾ TIME

**First and Second Endings**

Play the first ending. Repeat.
Skip the first ending and play the second ending.

**D.C. (*Da Capo*) al Fine**

Go back to the beginning (*Da Capo*) and stop at the end (*Fine*).

**1. Henry Martin**

Scottish Ballad

**2. Appalachian Folktune**

**3. Surfing**

*D. C. al Fine*

# III INTERVALS AND TUNING

## INTERVALS

An interval is the distance between two notes.

1. The smallest interval is called a minor second. A minor second interval is also called a half step. Half steps may be marked ⌃ or ⌄. The half steps you have been playing are:

**a. Major Fingering Pattern**

**b. Minor Fingering Pattern**

2. Two half steps equal a whole step.
A whole step is also called an interval of a major second. Whole steps may be marked by ⌞⌟ or ⌜⌝.

**a. Major Fingering Pattern**

**b. Minor Fingering Pattern**

3. Intervals between the tones in a **D Major Scale**.

**a. Whole Steps and Half Steps**      **b. Major Seconds and Minor Seconds**

4. Lines and spaces are numbered in sequence. Intervals are also named in sequence.

**a. Lines & spaces numbered beginning with "D."**      **b. The intervals named from the key note "D."**

| Interval: | 1st | 2nd | 3rd | 4th | 5th | 6th | 7th | 8th |
|---|---|---|---|---|---|---|---|---|
| Name: | Unison | Major second | Major third | Perfect fourth | Perfect fifth | Major sixth | Major seventh | Perfect octave |

5. Intervals of a major scale (D Major):

| Unison | Major Second | Major Third | Perfect Fourth | Perfect Fifth | Major Sixth | Major Seventh | Octave |

> Use the melodies on pages 6 and 7 to find and identify intervals of the major and minor second and the major third.

*Writing Music*
93VN

Turn to page 46, line #1. Follow the directions.

## INTERVAL STUDIES

**1. Perfect Fourths**

**2. Perfect Fifths**

**3. Octaves**

## TUNING

The strings on your instrument need to be tuned before each playing session. You will need a piano or a tuner to sound the correct reference pitch that corresponds to each of your open strings.

The pegs are turned when you need to make large adjustments in pitch.

The fine tuners are turned when you need to make small adjustments in pitch.

1. Hold the instrument with the peg box up and turned so that you are looking directly at the strings.
2. Sound the reference pitch, pluck the corresponding string and decide if the string sounds too high, too low, or just right.
3. With one hand plucking the string and the other hand turning the peg or the fine tuner, tune the string to match the reference pitch.
   - To raise the pitch: Turn the top of the peg away from you or turn the fine tuner clockwise.
   - To lower the pitch: Turn the top of the peg toward you or turn the fine tuner counter-clockwise.

**4. Tuning Tune**

Make up your own *Tuning Tune*.

# IV THE KEYS OF D, C, AND G MAJOR

A **key** is determined by sharps or flats called a **key signature**. The key signature appears at the beginning of a piece and tells which notes are to be raised or lowered for the entire piece.

A **scale** is a series of notes written or played stepwise in ascending or descending order with a specific sequence of whole steps and half steps determined by the key or key signature.

When the sequence is played in this order, it is called a **major scale**. The first and last notes ore called the **keynotes**.

## KEY OF D MAJOR

In the key of **D Major**, F and C are sharped in the key signature. Play all F's as F♯ and all C's as C♯. The **scale of D Major** is in the key of D Major. It begins and ends on D. D is the keynote.

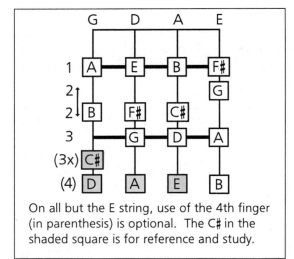

On all but the E string, use of the 4th finger (in parenthesis) is optional. The C♯ in the shaded square is for reference and study.

x=Extend the finger without moving the hand.

### 1. D Major Scale

Play the D Major Scale using two eighth notes on several of the tones. Change the bowing so that you include some slurs. Change the amount of bow you use. Alternate between forte and piano.

### 2. Finger Twister

### 3. Can-Can

Jacques Offenbach

(4)

In the key of **C Major**, there are no sharps in the key signature.
The **scale of C Major** is in the key of C Major. It begins and ends on C.  C is the keynote.

On all but the E string, use of the 4th finger (in parenthesis) is optional.  The F in the shaded square is for reference and study.

## 1. C Major Scale

## 2. C Major Scale Study

WB = Whole Bow: Use all of the bow.  UH= Upper half of the bow.  LH = Lower half of the bow.  *Similé* = Keep playing the same way.

## 3. Pop Goes the Weasel

English Folk Song

BOWING: For half notes move the bow slowly.  For quarter notes move the bow quickly.

FINGERING:  + Pluck the string with the left hand finger indicated.

Play *Pop Goes the Weasel* as written.  Play it again adding several notes to the melody wherever you feel they will sound good.  Play your improvisation while everyone else plays the melody.  The improvisation must "fit" with the melody.

*Improvising Music*

## KEY OF G MAJOR

In the key of **G Major**, F is sharped in the key signature. This means play all F's as F#. The **scale of G Major** is in the key of G Major. It begins and ends on G. G is the keynote.

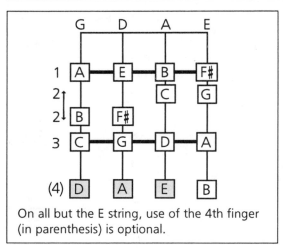

On all but the E string, use of the 4th finger (in parenthesis) is optional.

### 1. G Major Scales

### 2. Buffalo Gals

American Cowboy Song

### 3. Jonah and the Whale

American Spiritual

Turn to page 46, line #2. Follow the directions.

*Writing Music*

# Arpeggios in D, C, and G Major

| | |
|---|---|
| **Chord** | Three or more pitches played at the same time. |
| **Arpeggio** | Notes of a chord played one at a time. |

**DYNAMICS**

| | | |
|---|---|---|
| **Crescendo** | *cresc.* or ⊲ | Gradually become louder. |
| **Diminuendo** | *dim.* or ⊳ | Gradually become softer. |

**Accent**     >     Stress the beginning of the tone.

## 1. Building Arpeggios

## 2. Good Morning to You

American Camp Song

*Improvising Music*

Play *Good Morning to You.*  Improvise with your own notes every time you come to a half note.

## 3. Nelly Bly–Duet

Stephen Foster

# V FIVE NOTE MAJOR & MINOR FINGERING PATTERNS

## FINGERING DIAGRAMS, NOTATION, AND ILLUSTRATIONS

### MAJOR FINGERING PATTERN

MAJOR PATTERN
FOUR FINGERS DOWN

MINOR PATTERN
FOUR FINGERS DOWN

### MINOR FINGERING PATTERN

## Major and Minor Fingering Pattern Melodies

**1. Finger Strengthening Exercise** – *Left Hand Pizzicato*     *Violin and Viola only.*

**2. Ode to Joy**                                                                          Ludwig van Beethoven

Major Fingering Pattern

**3. The Birch Tree**                                                                          Russian Folk Song

Minor Fingering Pattern

*Improvising Music*

Improvise a melody on one string using the **major** fingering pattern.  Play your melody again changing it to the **minor** fingering pattern.

# VI MINOR MODES

## THE NATURAL MINOR SCALE AND MODAL MELODIES

The sequence of whole steps and half steps for a **natural minor** key is:

When the sequence is played in this order, it is called a **natural minor scale**. Another formula for the minor scale is to raise the sixth and seventh tones one half step.

### 1. Natural Minor Scale in E and Arpeggio

### 2. The Ghost of John - E Minor

English Folk Song

*Second time play pizzicato*

### 3. O Chanukah - A Minor

Israeli Folk Song

### 4. The Days of Knights - Duet in D Minor

# VII BASIC BOWING STYLES

## LEGATO AND STACCATO

**LEGATO** - The notes sound connected.
  **Détaché** - Broad, alternating bow strokes smoothly connected.
  **Slur** - Two or more notes of different pitch played with one bow stroke.
**STACCATO** - The notes sound separated and are marked by a dot above or below the notehead.
  **Martelé** - Separated bow strokes.  The bow remains **ON** the string.
  **Spiccato** - Separated bow strokes.  The bow bounces **OFF** the string.  Brush the string with the bow.

## Theme and Variations

### Theme - Détaché

Hungarian Folk Song

### Variation 1 - Slurs

### Variation 2 - Martelé

### Variation 3 - Détaché and Slurs

### Variation 4 - Spiccato

Improvise your own variation on the Hungarian folk song theme.  Try to use at least two different bowing styles.

## Melodies with Détaché, Slur, Martelé, and Spiccato Bowings

**1. Rippling Rhythm**   *Détaché and Slurs*

Turn to page 46, line #3.  Follow the directions.

**2. Folk Song**   *Spiccato*   Czech Folk Song

**3. Whiz Bang!**   *Martelé and Détaché*

### 4. The Ferris Wheel   *Slurs and Détaché*

### 5. Calypso Duet   *Martelé and Détaché*

Note: The bow remains on the string except at the rest before letter B and at the end.

Turn to page 46, line #4.  Follow the directions.

93VN

# VIII TIME AND RHYTHM STUDIES

## COMMON TIME AND CUT TIME

### 1. Rhythm Study

*Play on each open string.*

### 2. Ten Little Children

Spiritual

### 3. Knick-Knack Paddy Whack

American Folk Song

### 4. The Saints - Duet or Trio

New Orleans Jazz Tune

*Improvising Music*

93VN

Play *The Saints* as written.  Improvise your own notes and rhythm between letters A and B and from letter C to the end.

## DOTTED QUARTER AND EIGHTH NOTES

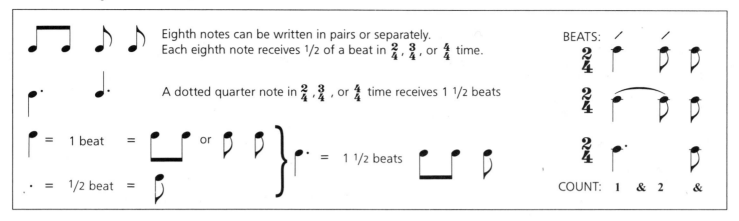

### 1. Rhythm Study    *Play on each open string.*

### 2. Etude

After learning each line, play the lines together as a duet.

### 3. Deep and Wide

Spiritual

*Improvising Music*

Improvise on *Deep and Wide* while someone plays the keyboard accompaniment with you.

### 4. Auld Lang Syne

Scottish Folk Song

# THE TRIPLET

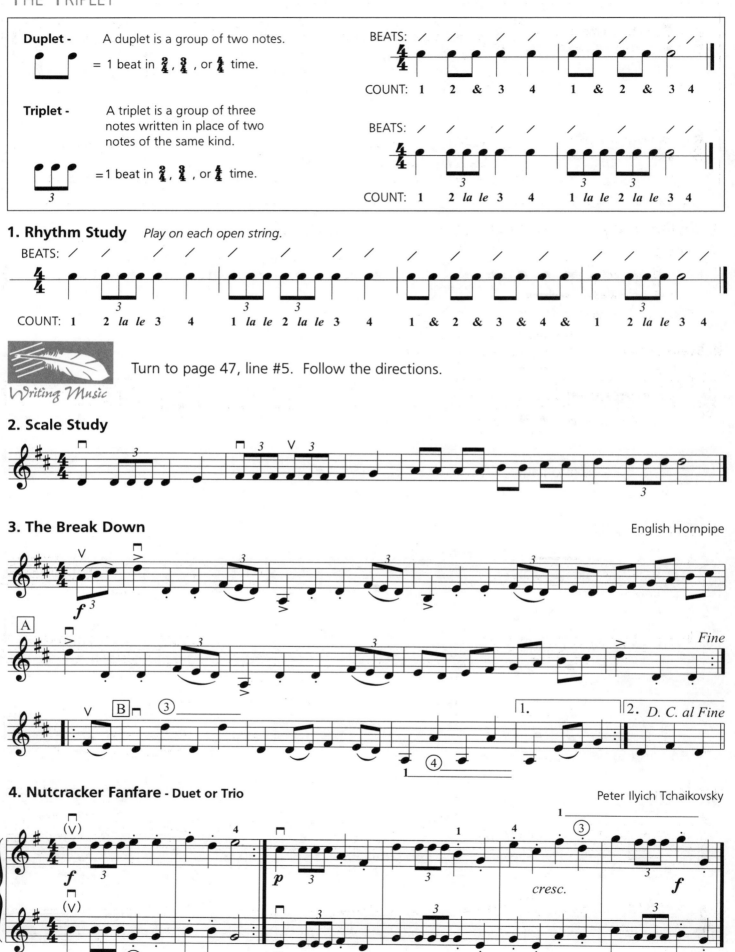

**1. Rhythm Study**  *Play on each open string.*

Turn to page 47, line #5.  Follow the directions.

*Writing Music*

**2. Scale Study**

**3. The Break Down**

English Hornpipe

*Fine*

**4. Nutcracker Fanfare - Duet or Trio**

Peter Ilyich Tchaikovsky

# $\frac{6}{8}$ Time

## 1. Rhythm Study

*Play on each open string.*

Hooked Bowing

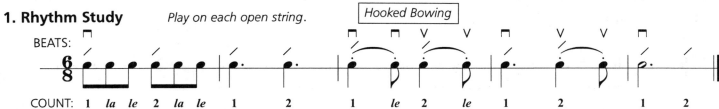

## 2. Scale Study

*First time: 6 beats in a measure.*
*Second time: 2 beats in a measure.*

*Writing Music*

Turn to page 47, line # 6.  Follow the directions.

## 3. River Boat Song

Sea Chantey

## 4. El Gavilan

Mexican Folk Song

# IX BACK EXTENSION

## DIAGRAM, NOTATION, AND MELODIES

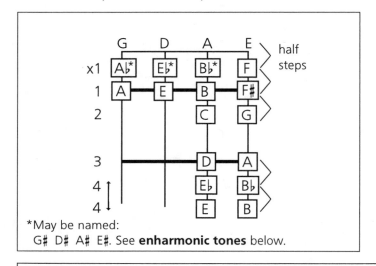

*May be named:
G♯ D♯ A♯ E♯. See **enharmonic tones** below.

x1 = Extend the first finger back toward the nut a half step. The first finger slides back and forth while the hand, including the thumb, remains in place. 4 ← → 4 = The fourth finger slides back and forth.

### ENHARMONIC TONES

Enharmonic tones - Tones with two names which sound the same but are written differently.

## 1. Sliding Around

*Slide the 1st finger on the A string.*

*Slide the 1st finger on the E string.*

A natural (♮) before a note indicates that note is neither flat or sharp.

## 2. Marching Back

*D. C. al Fine*

## 3. Jazz Blues Scale

*Improvising Music*

Play the *Jazz Blues Scale* on page 24.  Improvise any way you like using those notes.

**4. Back Again!**

*Writing Music*

Turn to page 47, line #7.  Follow the directions.

**5. Wiggle Worm**

**6. Chicken Feed**

# X THE KEYS OF F AND Bb MAJOR
# WITH RELATIVE MINORS

## F MAJOR

In the key of **F Major**, B is flat in the key signature. This means play all B's as Bb. The **scale of F Major** is in the key of F Major. It begins and ends on F. F is the keynote.

### 1. F Major Scale and Arpeggio

### 2. Folk Song

Czech Folk Song

### 3. Bicycle Built for Two

Henry Dacre

*Improvising Music*

Play *Bicycle Built for Two* as written. Improvise your own notes every time you come to the last two measures of each line of music (the end of each phrase).

# D Minor

In the key of **D Minor**, B is flat in the key signature.  This means play all B's as B♭.  The **scale of D Minor** is in the key of D Minor.  It begins and ends on D.  D is the keynote.

Major and minor keys with the same key signature are called "related keys."

## 1. D Minor Scale and Arpeggio

## 2. The Moldau Theme

Bedřich Smetana

**Smooth and flowing**

## 3. Canon

Hungarian Folk Song

## 4. When Johnny Comes Marching Home

Louis Lambert

**With spirit**

Turn to page 48, line #8.  Follow the directions.

*Writing Music*

# B♭ Major

In the key of **B♭ Major**, B and E are flat in the key signature.  This means play all B's and E's as B♭ and E♭.  The **scale of B♭ Major** is in the key of B♭ Major.  It begins and ends on B♭.  B♭ is the keynote.

## B♭ Major Scale and Arpeggio

### 2. Santa Lucia

Italian Folk Song

### 3. Barbara Allen - Duet or Trio

English Folk Song

# G MINOR

In the key of **G Minor**, B and E are flat in the key signature.  This means play all B's and E's as B♭ and E♭.  The **scale of G Minor** is in the key of G Minor.  It begins and ends on G.  G is the keynote.

**Tempo** - The speed at which music is performed.

**Steady tempo indicators:**
**Allegro** – Lively beat
**Andante** – Moderate walking beat

**Changing tempo indicators:**
***Ritardando*** ( *Rit.*) - Slow down the beat gradually.
***Accelerando*** ( Accel.) - Speed up the beat gradually.

***a tempo*** - Play at the original speed.

### 1. G Minor Scale and Arpeggio

 Play the *G Minor Scale and Arpeggio*.  Improvise any way you like using these notes.

### 2. Hey! Ho! Nobody Home

Canon

### 3. At the Hour of Midnight (A la Media Noche)

Puerto Rican Carol

### 4. Blues Rock

# XI FORWARD EXTENSION

## DIAGRAM, NOTATION, AND MELODIES

3x = Extend the third finger toward the bridge one half step. The third finger slides back and forth while the hand remains in place.

**1. Scale Patterns**

**2. Au Clair de la Lune**

French Folk Song

**A String Variation**

*Spiccato*

*Improvising Music*

Improvise your own variation to *Au Claire de la Lune*.

**3. Moveable Major Scale**

This one-octave scale fingering may be used to play all major scales on any two adjacent strings. Always begin with the first finger.

**4. Irish Reel**

Traditional Dance

A MAJOR

# XII THE KEY OF A MAJOR

In the key of A Major, F, C, and G are sharped in the key signature. This means play all F's, C's, and G's as F#, C#, and G#. The **scale of A Major** is in the key of A Major. It begins and ends on A. A is the keynote.

## 1. A Major Scale

## 2. Music Lives!

Traditional Round

## 3. Rhythm Study    *Play on each open string.*

## 4. La Raspa!

Mexican Folk Song

Alternate fingering with a lowered fourth finger.

*Writing Music*

Turn to page 48, line #9. Follow the directions.

# XIII Sixteenth Notes

Sixteenth Notes [♪♪♪♪] = 1 beat     Each sixteenth note receives 1/4 of a beat.

## 1. Rhythm Study     *Play on each open string.*     Use whole bows on the quarter notes.

BEATS:
COUNT:   1   a   &   a   2       1   a   &   a   2       1   &   2   a   &   a       1       2

## 2. D Major Scale Study

## 3. Little Bells of Westminster     Round

**Andante**

*Writing Music*     Turn to page 48, line #10.  Follow the directions.

## 4. Rhythm Study     *Play on each open string.*

BEATS:
COUNT:   1   &   a   2   &   a     1   &   a   2   &   a     1   &   a   2   &   a     1   &   2   &

## 5. Boil That Cabbage Down     Fiddle Tune
**Allegro**     This tune may be played with the open A string as a drone.

*f*

*Repeat twice*

*accel. last time*

## 6. William Tell Theme     Gioacchino Rossini
**Allegro**

*f*

## 7. Rhythm Study    *Play on each open string.*

## 8. Country Folk Song    Czech Folk Song

**Moderately fast**

## 9. Rhythm Study    *Play on each open string.*

## 10. Dinah Won't You Blow Your Horn    Traditional

**Moderately fast**

Play the melody of *Dinah Won't You Blow Your Horn* as written.  Improvise your own notes when you get to the quarter notes and quarter rests.

*Improvising Music*

# XIV HARMONIZED MELODIES

## AMERICA
### Three Part Harmony*

*Each section may divide with half playing the melody part and half playing the ensemble part.

# WE SHALL OVERCOME
## Three Part Harmony*

**MELODY PART**

American Song

**ENSEMBLE PART**

*Each section may divide with half playing the melody part and half playing the ensemble part.

# AMARYLLIS
## Three Part Harmony*

Henri Ghys

*Each section may divide with half playing the melody part and half playing the ensemble part.

# Menuetto
## Duet

Wolfgang Amadeus Mozart

Note: This arrangement may be played by all string instruments as an ensemble or by any two instruments as a duet.
*Light and lively, slightly slower than Allegro.

93VN

# SURPRISE SYMPHONY THEME
## Three Part Harmony*

**MELODY PART**

Franz Joseph Haydn

*Each section may divide with half playing the melody part and half playing the ensemble part.

(*Surprise Symphony* Theme, cont.)

**ENSEMBLE PART**

# MILITARY MARCH
Three Part Harmony*

**MELODY PART**

Franz Schubert

*Each section may divide with half playing the melody part and half playing the ensemble part.

(*Military March*, cont.)

**ENSEMBLE PART**

**March tempo**

# AMERICAN FIDDLE TUNE MEDLEY
## Duet

**Moderate Square Dance Tempo**

Traditional

Note: This arrangement may be played by all string instruments as an ensemble or by any two instruments as a duet.

(*Medley*, cont.)

E *"Arkansas Traveler"*

# XV HARMONICS AND VIBRATO

## LEARNING TO PLAY HARMONICS

Tones are produced on a string instrument by bowing or plucking:
1. **Open Strings**
2. **Stopped Tones** - Notes produced by pressing the string down with a finger
3. **Harmonic Tones** - Notes produced by lightly touching a string at a node

A **node** is a point where the string divides into harmonic segments.

**1. The First Harmonic**
Place your finger at the 1/2 node or halfway between the nut and the bridge. Lightly touch the string.

This harmonic sounds like:

Harmonic Notation

**2. The Second Harmonic**
Place your finger at the 1/3 node or 1/3 of the way from the nut to the bridge. Lightly touch the string.

This harmonic sounds like:

Harmonic Notation

**1. First Harmonic on D** | **Sul** means to play entirely on the string named.

**2. First Harmonic on A**

**3. Harmonics on Each String** | Play the harmonics with any finger.

**4. Harmonic Etude** | Carefully observe the difference between the "stopped" tones and the "harmonic" tones.

# LEARNING TO PLAY WITH VIBRATO

**Vibrato** is a slight, constant change of pitch on sustained tones. It is used to enhance the tone and expressive qualities of a musical instrument. On a string instrument, it is produced by a steady back and forth motion of the finger, wrist, and arm.

Producing the vibrato motion:
1. Find and play the second harmonic (at the 1/3 node) with your first finger.
2. Keeping your thumb in place, slide your finger back about a half inch from the location of the harmonic and then returnto the point where the harmonic is best produced. Your finger should feel as though it is polishing the string.
3. Continue the back and forth motion slowly at first. Increase the speed slightly keeping the hand relaxed and the motion steady. Fingers of the left hand touch the instrument in only two places:
    a) The thumb touches the neck of the instrument
    b) One finger at a time touches a string.
4. Try this motion with your 2nd, 3rd, and 4th fingers on the first harmonic (at the 1/2 node).

〰〰〰   means to produce the slow the vibrato motion

**1. Sul D Vibrato**    | Slide your finger back and forth only on the notes indicated. Use whole bows. |

**2. Sul A Vibrato**    | Slide your finger back and forth only on the notes indicated. Use whole bows. |

**3.** Continuing to make the harmonic tone, play #1 and #2 by moving your hand back and forth so that your finger is **rolling** on its tip.

**4.** Play #1 and #2 by **lightly pressing** the string to the fingerboard. You are now playing a stopped tone rather than a harmonic tone. Continue to move your hand back and forth so that the finger is **rolling** on its tip. Be sure that only one finger at a time touches the string and that the side of your left hand is not touching the neck of the instrument.

**5.** Move your hand a step at a time toward first position. Play a slow vibrato on each finger. Try this on all four strings.

**6. Vibrato in First Position**

**7. Vibrato Etude**   Try to produce a slow vibrato on each half, dotted half, and whole note (except for open string notes).

**Play Slowly**

# XVI WRITING MUSIC

1. Copy the ascending and descending D Major scale and name the notes. Reminder: notes placed above the middle line have stems going down and are positioned to the right of the notehead. Notes placed below the middle line have stems going up and are positioned to the left of the notehead.

**Ascending D Major Scale**                    **Descending D Major Scale**

**Names:** ___  ___  ___  ___  ___  ___  ___  ___  ___  ___  ___  ___  ___  ___  ___  ___

2. Play measures 1 and 3 then compose your own music for measures 2 and 4. Write the music that you composed. Play the entire piece.

3. Complete this melody. End your melody on G. Play what you composed.

4. Write your own melody using either the $\frac{2}{4}$ or the $\frac{3}{4}$ time signature in the key of C. Before you start composing, place the clef sign and time signature on the staff. Start and end your melody on C.

5. Write an ascending and descending C Major scale with a triplet for each tone of the scale in the $\frac{2}{4}$ time signature. Play what you have written.

*ascending*

*descending*

6. Copy measures 1 and 2 in measures 3 and 4. Compose your own music in measures 6, 7, and 8. Play your music.

7. Practice making flat, sharp, and natural signs.

Copy measures 1, 2, and 3 in measures 5, 6, and 7. Play your music.

8. Write your own melody in the key of D Minor using the $\frac{2}{4}$, $\frac{4}{4}$, or $\frac{6}{8}$ time signature. Before you start to compose, place the clef sign, the key signature, and the time signature on the staff. Start and end your melody on D.

9. Write an ascending and a descending A Major scale in $\frac{4}{4}$ time. For each tone of the scale use this rhythm: ♪ ♪ ♪. Play the scale.

*ascending*

*descending*

10. Write your own melody in D Major using the $\frac{4}{4}$ time signature. Try to use a few groups of (four sixteenth notes). Before you begin composing, place the clef sign, the key signature, and the time signature on the staff. Start and end your melody on D.

Now you are ready to compose more music. You will need a music manuscript book for your composing. Think of the pieces you enjoyed playing. Look at how they were written. Try to write something similar. Think of the rhythms you like and use them in your compositions. If you are not satisfied with your composition, just turn the page and start over. GOOD LUCK!